What Shall We Eat?

GO Green

Helen Lanz

FRANKLIN WATTS
LONDON • SYDNEY

This edition 2012

First published in 2010 by
Franklin Watts
338 Euston Road
London NW1 3BH

Franklin Watts Australia
Level 17/207 Kent Street
Sydney NSW 2000

Series editor: Julia Bird
Design: D.R. ink
Artworks: Mike Phillips

A CIP catalogue record for this book is available
from the British Library.

ISBN 978 1 4451 0916 9
Dewey classification: 641.3'02

Picture credits: Ralf Antblad/istockphoto: 9t: Paul Barton/Corbis:
front cover t;Mark Boulton/Alamy: 25cr; Brazil Photos/Alamy: 18t;
Alan Crawford/istockphoto: 1, 13t; Digital Vision/Getty Images: 8;
Esemelwe/istockphoto: 11b: Fotocraft/Alamy: 26;
Simon Hadley/Alamy: 21; Helicefoto/istockphoto: front cover cr;
Dana Hoff/Corbis: 17t; Imagebroker/Alamy: 25bl;
Image Source Pink/Alamy: 19b; Jaileybug/Alamy: 24;
Linda Kennedy/Alamy: 20t; Richard Levine/Alamy: 27t;
Pavel Losevsky/Shutterstock: 16; Luoman/istockphoto: 10:
Robin Mackenzie/Shutterstock: 13b; Manor Photography/Alamy: 20b;
© Marine Stewardship Council: 19t; Karl Marttila/Alamy: 14tr;
Monkey Business Images/Shutterstock: 27b; Photospin Inc/Alamy: 14bl;
Pot of Grass Productions/Shutterstock: 7t; Paul Prescott/Alamy: 12;
Viorika Prikhodko/istockphoto: 6; Mark Ross/Shutterstock: 23b;
Alex Segre/Alamy: 22; US Stock Images/Alamy: 7b.
Vegware Ltd/vegware.co.uk: 23t; Peter Viisimaa/istockphoto: 9b;
Joao Vinissimo/Shutterstock: 18b; Alison Wright/Corbis: 11t.
Sergey Zavalnyuk/Alamy: 15.

Printed in China

Franklin Watts is a division of Hachette Children's Books,
an Hachette UK company.
www.hachette.co.uk

To Rache for our inherited and shared love of cooking.

> "During 25 years of writing about the environment for the Guardian, I quickly realised that education was the first step to protecting the planet on which we all depend for survival. While the warning signs are everywhere that the earth is heating up and the climate changing, many of us have been too preoccupied with living our lives to notice what is going on in our wider environment. It seems to me that it is children who need to know what is happening: they are often more observant of what is going on around them. We need to help them to grow up respecting and preserving the natural world on which their future depends. By teaching them about the importance of water, energy and other key areas of life, we can be sure they will soon be influencing their parents' lifestyles, too. This is a series of books every child should read."

Paul Brown

Former environment correspondent for the *Guardian*, environmental author and fellow of Wolfson College, Cambridge.

Contents

Words in **bold** can be found in the glossary on page 28.

Where does our food come from?

What have you eaten today? A piece of fruit, a sandwich, or maybe a biscuit or two? Have you ever really thought about where the food we eat comes from, how it gets to us or what happens to any food that is left over?

Fresh food

The food that we buy in the shops comes from farms all over the world. Fruit, **cereal crops** and vegetables are grown in fields, orchards and greenhouses. Eggs and dairy products come from animals on farms, and meat comes from animals that have been specially bred for the purpose.

Many fruits, including apples, are ready to eat once they are ripe. No cooking or preparing is required!

Processed food

We eat some fresh foods, such as fruit and vegetables, in their raw state. But much of the food we buy today has been processed in some way. This means that it has been changed from its raw state, for example by cooking it, to make it into another food item or part of another food item, such as a packet of cereal or a tin of soup. Food processing takes place in factories.

 Once food has been packaged, it may need refrigerating, too.

Packaging and transporting

Once the food has been processed, it is packaged to make it easier to store and transport. It is also wrapped in plastic or foil to keep it fresh. It is then transported by road, sea or air to the shops and supermarkets where it will be sold.

CASE STUDY

IN THE BIN

In developed countries, we tend to take our food for granted, so much so that many of us waste a lot of food. In the UK, one out of every three shopping bags of food we buy is thrown away. That is not just packaging, but food that could actually still be eaten. In the US, one out of every four bags, and in Australia, one out of every five shopping bags of food is thrown away.

Imagine putting one third of this food straight into the bin.

The cost of food

You might think that the cost of your food is simply the money you hand over to buy it. But the real cost is much more complicated and expensive than that!

An expensive process

Growing our food, processing it, packaging it, storing some of it in refrigerators and finally transporting it to the shops where it will be sold, all of these activities have another cost – a cost to our **environment**.

Fossil fuels

The factories that process and wrap food products use electricity. Electricity is usually made by burning fuels such as coal, natural gas or oil. Transporting food also uses fuel, usually petrol or diesel. All of these fuels are known as **fossil fuels** because they were formed underground over millions of years from plant or animal remains. Earth's fossil fuels cannot be replaced and will eventually run out.

The more a food is processed, the more **energy** is used.

Global warming

Burning fossil fuels creates a gas called **carbon dioxide** (CO_2). Carbon dioxide is known as a **greenhouse gas** because it traps heat from the Sun inside the Earth's atmosphere, just like glass traps heat in a greenhouse. The atmosphere is the layer of air that surrounds the Earth. The extra CO_2 in the atmosphere is making the Earth heat up – this is called **global warming**.

Greenhouses trap the heat of the Sun to provide a warm place to grow plants.

Did you know?

Around 20% of greenhouse gases are related to the production, processing, transportation and storage of food.

Extreme weather has extreme results: this river has broken its banks.

Climate change

Earth's climate varies naturally, but evidence shows that people have made it change more quickly by burning more fossil fuels. As the temperature of the Earth changes, it changes our weather patterns. This is called **climate change**. Extreme weather events around the world, such as floods, droughts and powerful storms, are becoming more common.

The price of farming

Farming gives us food and influences how we use and look after the countryside, but it can also cause problems for the environment.

Disappearing forests

As the world's **population** increases year on year, more food is needed. As a result, more and more forest around the world is being changed into farmland where farmers can grow crops and raise cattle. This is known as **deforestation**. The **rainforest** in countries such as Brazil is being cleared at a rate of 36 football pitches a minute to use for farming and industry. Deforestation is damaging the world's natural environment, as it contributes to global warming, removes animals' **habitats** and can cause local flooding.

More and more areas of forest are being cut down to provide land to grow crops or pasture to graze animals.

Did you know?

When cattle digest grass, they produce a greenhouse gas called methane. Methane is over 20 times more damaging than CO_2.

BREATHING TREES

Rainforests are precious for many reasons. They are the natural habitat of many species of insects and animals. They are a source of many natural ingredients for medicines. And trees use CO_2 to grow – so they absorb, or take in, a lot of the CO_2 that we create through burning fossil fuels. But if we cut more and more trees down, we lose this natural way to balance our actions.

The rainforests can be harvested for vital ingredients to make medicines.

Fertilisers and pesticides

Many farmers use chemicals such as **fertilisers** and **pesticides** on their crops. Fertilisers help crops to grow, and pesticides protect crops from insects and diseases. Both of these can be washed into local rivers, lakes and ponds where they can kill wildlife and pollute drinking water. They also sink into the soil, where they build up over time and make the soil less **fertile**.

The pesticide spray from a tractor covers the soil as well as the crops. It can seep down into the ground and get into our **groundwater**.

Food miles

Did you know that in order to reach your plate, your food could have travelled over 2,000 km? Supermarkets today sell food from all over the world. This means that we can choose from a variety of food all year round, but our food's journey also has a big environmental cost.

Transport toll

If the food you are eating has been grown locally, it might not have had far to travel, but nowadays food is often grown in a different country from where it is eaten. Transporting food from one country to another uses huge amounts of fuel and so creates a lot of CO_2.

 Some bananas eaten in the UK have travelled from India – a journey of over 8,000 km!

Farm to fork

Food miles try to measure how far our food has travelled from 'farm to fork' – that is from the fields where it is grown to our plate. Food miles are based on how much CO_2 our food has made along its journey, including the fertiliser it took to grow it, the fuel it took to transport it, the energy it used to process and store it in the shop, and so on.

Grow abroad

For some foods, in terms of food miles, it may be better to grow them abroad. In the UK for example, tomatoes are usually grown in greenhouses or polytunnels in the winter. It takes a lot of fuel to heat the greenhouses or polytunnels, so it can be more environmentally friendly to grow them in a warmer country, such as Spain, and then transport them to the UK.

Polytunnels are plastic shelters that can be used to grow a variety of foods, in particular soft fruits.

FOOD MILE FACTS

The average Christmas dinner travels about 50,000 km – that's all the way round the Earth, and a little bit more!

A study in the USA showed that the ingredients of strawberry yoghurt – strawberries, milk and sugar – had travelled over 3,540 km before reaching the supermarket.

How far has your pudding travelled?

What a waste!

Every day around the world, millions of tonnes of leftover food is thrown away. Throwing food away is not just a waste of money, it also pollutes our environment and contributes to the problem of global warming.

Wasting away

Developed countries are the worst culprits when it comes to throwing away food. It is estimated that in the USA, 25 million tonnes of food are thrown away every year – that's enough to fill the Rose Bowl (a huge sports stadium) every three days. In the UK, 6.7 million tonnes of food is thrown away a year – this includes one million slices of ham, 1.3 million yoghurts and enough apples to fill 12 double decker buses *a day*. Australians throw out three million tonnes of food a year – enough to feed the whole country for three weeks.

 Can you imagine this enormous stadium filled with unwanted food? What a waste.

Hidden costs

This isn't just a waste of food, it's also a waste of the **natural resources** taken to grow the food. To grow the three million tonnes of food thrown away in Australia a year wastes enough water to fill Sydney Harbour three times! Throwing food away also wastes a lot of money. In the UK, families spend over £420 a year on food that is simply thrown away. And it wastes space: nearly one fifth of food waste in the USA ends up in **landfill**.

A lot of our waste, including food scraps, ends up being buried in the ground in landfill. Rotting food gives off the greenhouse gas methane.

A source of pollution

Throwing so much food away also contributes to the worldwide problem of global warming. If the UK alone didn't waste the amount of food it does, it would save 18 million tonnes of CO_2 being released into the air each year. That's like taking one in five cars (whose exhaust fumes cause CO_2 pollution) off the roads.

WORRYING WASTE

In the USA, restaurants throw away more than 6,000 tonnes of food every day. In terms of weight, that's the same as 1,000 Asian male elephants.

Throwing away just one kilogram of white rice wastes 2,385 litres of water that went into making it. That's enough water to fill nearly 30 baths!

Waste not, want not

By reducing our food waste, we can save ourselves money, cause less pollution and use less energy. There are loads of things that we can do to reduce our food waste and you may do some of them already.

A cunning plan!

To start with, you could help to plan a week's menu with your family. By planning meals in advance, you are more likely to buy just the food you need, and if you help to choose what's on the menu, you're more likely to eat it too!

 Get involved and help out with the weekly food shop.

Sensible shopping

Once you've planned a week's menu, try to write a shopping list and take it with you when you go. Help out in the supermarket by checking 'sell by' and 'use by' dates. Buy food items with the latest date, so you have more time to use your ingredients and you don't end up throwing them away because they have gone rotten or mouldy.

Check the cupboard

Keep basic ingredients such as tinned tomatoes in the cupboard. Whoever does most of the cooking in your household will have their favourite ingredients and it is useful to have some basics that can be added to lots of different dishes. This will help use up leftovers and means you don't have to drive to the shop for just one item.

 Basic foods, such as rice and pasta, are always useful to have in the cupboard.

When I asked you to make something with the leftovers, I meant something we could eat!

Portion control!

Have you ever heard the expression 'Your eyes were bigger than your stomach?' This is when you put more food on your plate than you can eat. Try to only take what you need and no more. Be sure to eat at least your five portions of fruit and vegetables a day, though. But if you can't finish your meal, try turning your leftovers into creative dishes. There are lots of different recipes you could try, so look on the Internet with your parent or carer for ideas.

The choice is yours

We make many choices about our food that make a difference to our environment, from what we choose to eat to how often we go to the shops.

 These cattle in Brazil are grazing on land that used to be rainforest.

Meat and two veg

Did you know that due to the demand for beef, there are about 1.3 billion cattle on Earth? These cattle take up about a quarter of the land on the planet and they eat enough grain to feed millions of people. Raising this amount of cattle causes more CO_2 pollution than the pollution caused by transport and uses up a lot of our water supply. We don't have to stop eating beef, but for the benefit of our environment we should think about whether we need to eat as much beef as we do.

Did you know?

It is believed that every hamburger made from certain central American beef results in the loss to the rainforest of, on average, one large tree, about 50 saplings and 20–30 seedlings.

Shop with care

Shops can only sell what people will buy. If we all choose to buy food that has been grown with care, or packaged responsibly, this is another way to help our environment. Some people choose to eat **organic foods**, which are usually grown using more natural methods, reducing the amount of chemicals used to make crops grow or to control pests. However, growing organic crops does take up more land than growing crops using chemicals.

 Look out for the Marine Stewardship logo on fish and fish products.

Spot the symbol

Look out for the symbols or logos on packaging that show the food has been produced using environmentally friendly methods. For example the Marine Stewardship logo shows that the item has been fished from **sustainable** stocks.

Food ordered online saves a journey to the supermarket.

Get on-line

Did you know that in the UK, half of the distance clocked up in cars is from travelling to and from the supermarket? If your family has access to the Internet, try shopping on-line. Also, try to build up a list of things you need, rather than going to the shop for just one item.

It's in season for a reason!

When your grandma or grandad were young, less food was **imported** from other countries. This meant that people mostly ate food that was grown locally and was **in season**. This was better for the environment as it meant that the food grew naturally at that time of year and so needed less energy to make it grow.

Go local

Food that is grown in season and sold locally can be fresher, and often tastier, because it won't have had to travel far or be stored for long. Many supermarkets now offer locally-grown produce so you can choose foods that have taken less energy to grow, and clocked up fewer food miles along the way.

Farm shops sell fresh, locally-grown food such as fruit, vegetables, eggs and cheese.

CASE STUDY

COMPOSTING

As the food we throw out rots, it creates the greenhouse gas methane. But there is something we can do about this. Try not to put your food waste in the bin – compost it instead! Composting is when natural garden waste and food waste, such as fruit and vegetable scraps, tea bags and crushed egg shells, are mixed together and left to break down to make a natural fertiliser. This fertiliser can be used in the garden to make the soil richer. Up to half our household waste could be composted.

You can get compost bins from your local council or most DIY stores.

Grow your own

Why not try growing your own fruit and vegetables? You can't get much fresher than that! If you don't have a garden at home, perhaps you and your family could take on a local allotment or you could join or start a school gardening club.

 Growing your own can be great fun, as well as giving you fresh fruit and vegetables to eat.

When I said natural things could go in the compost, I didn't mean your brother!

WHAT ROT!

In Victoria in Australia, nearly half of waste sent to landfill is green or food waste, much of which could be composted.

Pack light

Today, more than half of all packaging is used to package food. But it is possible to help reduce the amount of packaging that ends up in landfill from our food products.

Less is more

When you go shopping, try to buy food items with less packaging. Try not to buy things that are individually wrapped, such as biscuits in separate wrappers, for example. Also, where possible, choose to buy food in packaging that can be **recycled**, or better still, buy food that's in recycled packaging that can be recycled!

These bananas don't need their plastic packaging - they have their skins to protect them!

GREENER PACKAGING

Some shops are trying to make their packaging more environmentally-friendly. Research has been done into finding a material that will rot or break down and so not take up space in landfill. The UK shop Marks & Spencer has already produced and sold over 132 million sandwiches packed in corn-based plastic packaging.

This sandwich packaging can be composted as it is made from corn.

Food packaging

To help decide what to do with any food packaging, look for labels on the packaging that can help you. If your sandwich has come in a corn-based packet, it may have a composting symbol on it so you know you can compost it safely. Plastics and glass often have the recycling triangle; where a number appears in the middle, this tells you how to group your plastics. The mobius loop is a well-known recycling symbol.

Did you know?

In 2006, 43,000 tonnes of green packaging was used worldwide – that's about the same weight as 6,000 fully-grown African elephants!

The mobius loop is used around the world to show that something can be recycled.

Get a bag habit!

Does your family take your own bags with you when you go shopping? If you don't, now is the time to get a 'bag habit'! Plastic bags are one of the biggest sources of pollution in the world and most of the time, they are used once and then thrown away.

'Take an old bag shopping'

People are becoming more concerned about the effect that throwing away billions of plastic shopping bags is having on our environment. 'Get a bag habit' or 'take an old bag shopping' are just a couple of the campaigns used by governments and supermarkets to encourage us to remember to take reusable bags with us when we do our food shop.

Did you know?
It is claimed that 8.7 plastic shopping bags contain enough petroleum energy in them to drive a car for one kilometre.

We may only use a plastic bag for a few minutes, but it can take up to 500 years for the bag to break down. And before it does, it can litter our countryside and endanger our wildlife.

BAGS GALORE

In the UK in 2008, 98,800 tonnes of bags were given out – that's enough to fill 188 Olympic swimming pools. On average, each adult uses 300 plastic bags a year. Twenty million Australians use an estimated 6.4 billion plastic bags every year. That's nearly one bag per person, per day, or 345 bags per person, per year.

Taxing bags

Some shops are doing their best to help solve the problem of people not reusing their plastic bags. Some now charge for every plastic bag to discourage people from taking more bags than they need. Some supermarkets also have boxes where you can recycle your plastic shopping bags.

 Plastic carrier bags can be recycled at many supermarkets.

CARRIER BAGS ONLY

Carrier bag RECYCLING

New products

Recycled plastic bags can be turned into new, and sometimes surprising products. If you're handy with a knitting needle, plastic bags can be made into new knitted reusable bags, blankets and rugs. Some artists have even turned plastic bags into works of art to draw attention to the problem of plastic bag waste.

 Artists have made these chicken ornaments out of plastic bags.

Power to the people!

Have you heard of the three Rs – reduce, reuse and recycle? Well, we can do that with food waste as well as general waste. We can reduce the amount we buy and eat, reuse our leftovers and recycle food packaging or any food waste by composting. And remember, if we all act together, we can make a big difference.

Less is best!

You can tell when Christmas is over because Easter eggs start to appear in the shops! If you celebrate Easter, you will probably look forward to getting some chocolate eggs. But how many times have you opened a chocolate Easter egg to find that it was mostly packaging?

Customers have started to complain about this, so companies who make the eggs, such as Nestlé, Cadbury's and Thorntons, have reduced their Easter egg packaging. The cuts Nestlé made in the UK in 2009 saved 700 tonnes of waste. Because there was less packaging, more eggs could also fit in the lorries, saving 77,249 km of road transport and so reducing the amount of CO_2 given off.

Companies do listen to public concern and have recently cut down on wasteful packaging.

MAKING THE MOST OF FOOD WASTE

In New York in the USA, a charity called **City Harvest** collects food waste from restaurants, shops, factories, and so on, and takes it to homeless shelters, soup kitchens and care centres to feed the hungry and homeless. In an average year, they collect 10.4 million kg of food a year. In December 2008, New York school children added 27,215 kg of food to this – that's heavier than 100 black bears!

Volunteers help to package apples for the homeless in a City Harvest project in Union Square, New York.

A wise choice

People power really can work. Use it wisely to try to encourage shops to sell food that has been grown in an environmentally-friendly way, packaged only when necessary, and with green packaging that can be composted. Use your own power wisely to make careful choices about what food you choose to eat and buy.

Remember to look at the labels before you buy your food to see if it has been grown in an environmentally-friendly way.

Glossary

Carbon dioxide A gas in the air around us.

Cereal crops Crops that are grown to produce grain, such as wheat.

Climate change Longterm changes to the world's weather patterns.

Deforestation The cutting down of large areas of forests by people.

Developed countries Countries that are wealthy and rely on money from industry; and where most people work in factories and businesses rather than in farming.

Energy The power to make or do something.

Environment Surroundings.

Fertile In this instance, land that can produce healthy crops.

Fertiliser A substance, either natural or chemical, that is given to plants or put on the land to make plants grow well.

Fossil fuels Fuels such as coal, oil or gas, which have developed under the ground from rotting animal and plant life over millions of years.

Global warming The gradual heating up of the Earth's atmosphere.

Greenhouse gas A gas, such as carbon dioxide, that creates an invisible layer around the Earth, keeping in the heat of the Sun's rays.

Groundwater Water that is held underground in rocks and soil.

Habitat The natural surroundings in which an animal or plant usually lives.

Imported When products or goods are brought in from one country to another.

In season In this instance, when a food is available during its natural growing time.

Landfill Areas for dumping and burying household or industrial waste.

Natural resources Materials, such as water and wood, that are found in nature.

Organic foods Foods that have been grown using natural methods, without relying on chemical fertilisers or pesticides.

Pesticides Chemicals used to kill unwanted pests and diseases on plants.

Population The number of people living in a place.

Processed In this instance, to do with adding chemicals to food in order to preserve, or keep it fresh, for longer.

Rainforest A forest in an area that usually receives a lot of rain.

Raw state In this instance, a food that hasn't been processed, or chemically changed in any way, but is eaten in the form in which it has grown.

Recycle To break something down so the materials it is made of can be used again.

Sustainable Able to be used now and in the future.

Useful information

Throughout this book, 'real life measurements' are used for reference. These measurements are not exact, but give a sense of just how much an amount is, or what it looks like.

1 full bath = 80 LITRES

American black bear = 270 KG

Asian elephant = 5,000 KG or 5 TONNES

African elephant = 7,000 KG or 7 TONNES

Olympic-sized swimming pool = 2,500,000 LITRES

Further reading

Food and Farming: From Farm To Table by Richard and Louise Spilsbury (Wayland, 2011)

Green Team: Your Food by Sally Hewitt (Franklin Watts 2011)

Grow Your Own series by Helen Lanz (Franklin Watts 2010)

Websites

www.lovefoodhatewaste.com
Recipes, food-saving tips and how to avoid waste.

www.greenchoices.org/?s=food
All about the choices we make about what we eat.

www.foodgloriousfood.org.uk
A fun website on growing your own food and eating local and seasonal food.

Dates to remember

Earth Hour – 31 March

Earth Day – 22 April

World Environment Day – 5 June

Clean Air Day – June

Walk to School Campaign – May and October

World Food Day – 16 October

Buy Nothing Day – 24 November

Note to parents and teachers: Every effort has been made by the Publishers to ensure that these websites are suitable for children, that they are of the highest educational value, and that they contain no inappropriate or offensive material. However, because of the nature of the Internet, it is impossible to guarantee that the contents of these sites will not be altered. We strongly advise that Internet access is supervised by a responsible adult

Index